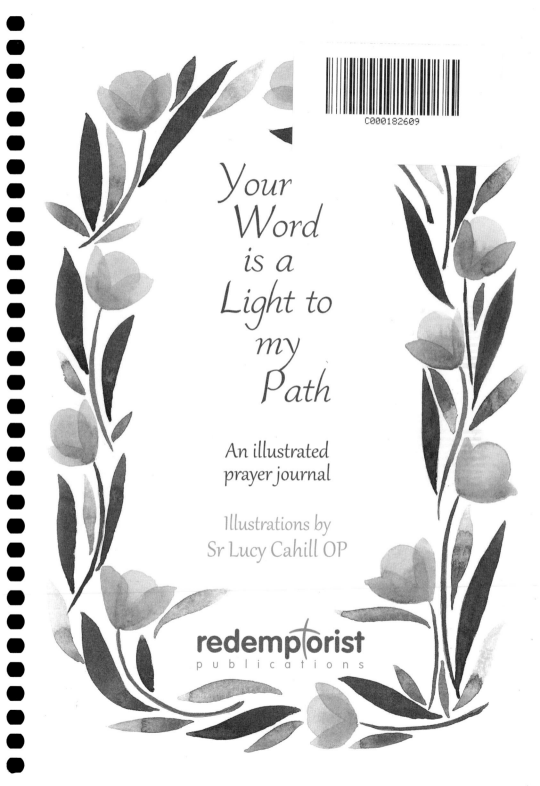

Your Word is a Light to my Path

An illustrated
prayer journal

Illustrations by
Sr Lucy Cahill OP

redemptorist
p u b l i c a t i o n s

This
Prayer Journal
belongs to

....

Introduction

"More than anything," writes poet Sally Read, "learning God's word is like falling in love."[1] This was certainly my experience when entering religious life. While I had considered myself reasonably familiar with the Bible and its contents, suddenly it was part of my daily life in a way it had not been previously: in study, in the apostolate of the sisters, in conversation and especially in the liturgy. Very often, a particular line or passage would leap out to me while praying the Divine Office in choir, and I would memorise the reference so that I could look it up later and spend more time pondering it.

I have been a journal-keeper for many years, and before entering the convent it had been my practice to make a point of writing down uplifting phrases or quotations that resonated with me in some way. As I continued this practice, slowly but surely my journals became filled with snippets of the Bible; words that were not only pleasant and inspirational but that carried eternal weight. While words of human authors can bring comfort and insight across the ages, the Bible is unique in that its words are not only human but also divine. When we read them and hear them, in all their beauty and strangeness, we are receiving words that were given to every member of the human race, across all times and places, but also and especially, specifically, to us here and now. For God's Word is not simply a collection of writings, but a Person: Jesus Christ. When we take the time to read the Bible, pondering it in our hearts, we come into intimate contact with the One who made us and loves us, and his love becomes alive in us.

This journal is a fruit of my own ponderings, but it is my hope that it will be able to play a part in bringing about fruits in the lives of those who use it. For me, calligraphy and watercolour painting is a way of meditating on the verses I am decorating; a way to prayerfully spend time with God's word while the designs take shape under my pens and brushes. Once complete, the illustrations and colours draw in those who look at them, but all in order to draw attention to the message at their heart. I pray that these images will aid you in hearing the Word of God speaking directly to you in your own life, bringing peace, guidance, and above all the knowledge that you are loved.

---

1 Sally Read, *Annunciation* (Ignatius Press, 2019), chapter 4.

God
saw all
he had
made,
and indeed
it was
very good.

Genesis 1:31

For I know the plans I have
for you, says the LORD,
plans for welfare, not for evil,
to give you a future and a hope.

JEREMIAH 29:11

The LORD will EXULT with JOY over you

ZEPHANIAH 3:17

FOR EVERYTHING
THERE IS A SEASON,
AND A TIME
FOR EVERY MATTER
UNDER HEAVEN...

ECCLESIASTES 3:1

the Almighty works marvels for me; HOLY His name!

LUKE 1:49

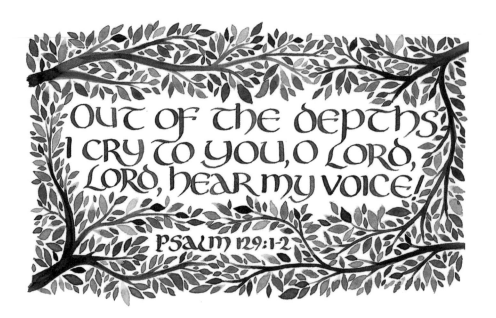

OUT OF THE DEPTHS
I CRY TO YOU, O LORD,
LORD, HEAR MY VOICE!

PSALM 129:1-2

Under
His eyes
I have found
true peace.

Song of Songs 8:9-10

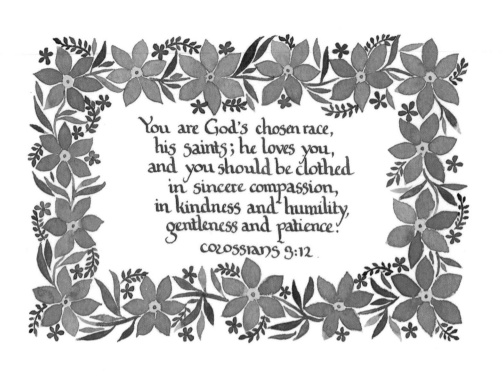

You are God's chosen race,
his saints; he loves you,
and you should be clothed
in sincere compassion,
in kindness and humility,
gentleness and patience.

COLOSSIANS 3:12

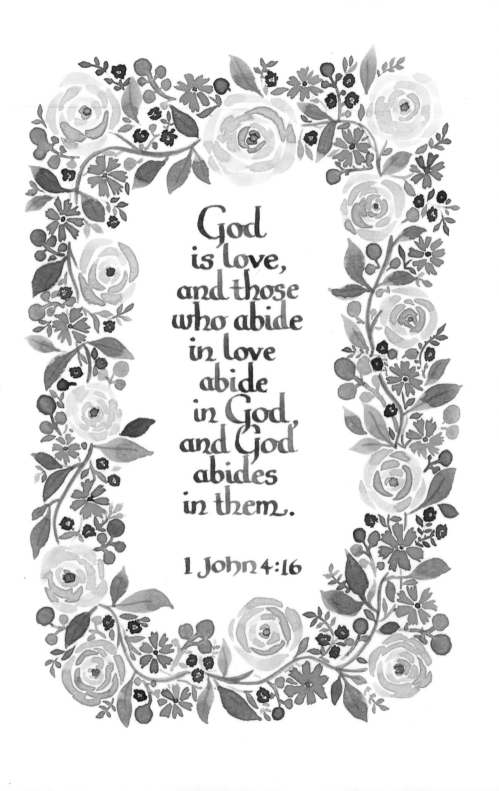

God
is love,
and those
who abide
in love
abide
in God,
and God
abides
in them.

1 John 4:16

I shall pour
clean water over you, and
you will be CLEANSED...
I shall remove the heart of stone
from your bodies and give you
a heart of flesh instead.

EZEKIEL
36:25.26

The
LORD
has
RISEN
indeed!
cf. Luke 24:34

Blessed are those
who hear the Word of God
and keep it!

cf. Luke 11:28

There are three
things that last:
FAITH,
hope
and
LOVE;
and the greatest
of these is
LOVE.

1 CORINTHIANS 13:13

Come to me,
all you who labour
and are overburdened,
and I will give you rest.
Shoulder my yoke
and learn from me,
for I am gentle and
humble in heart,
and you will find
rest for your souls.

Matthew 11:28-29

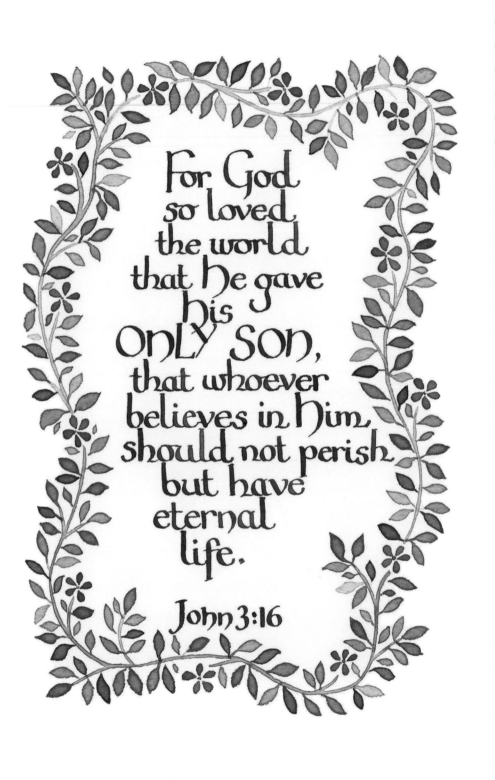

For God
so loved
the world
that He gave
his
ONLY SON,
that whoever
believes in Him,
should not perish,
but have
eternal
life.

John 3:16

For as the earth makes fresh things grow,
as a garden makes seeds spring up,
so will the LORD make both integrity & praise
spring up in the sight of the nations.

ISAIAH 61:11

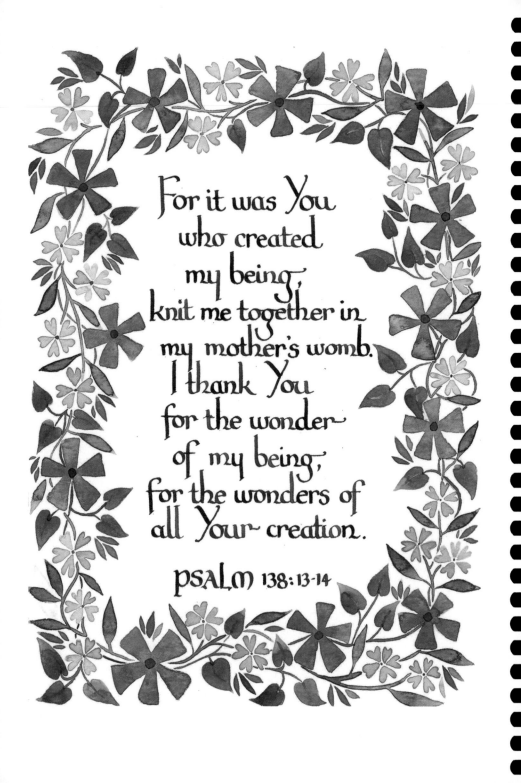

For it was You
who created
my being,
knit me together in
my mother's womb.
I thank You
for the wonder
of my being,
for the wonders of
all Your creation.

PSALM 138:13-14

I call you friends, because I have made known to you everything I have learnt from My Father.

JOHN 15:15

"I am the handmaid of the LORD," said Mary, "let what you have said be done to me."

LUKE 1:38

MAY GOD OUR FATHER
AND THE
LORD JESUS CHRIST
SEND YOU
GRACE AND PEACE.

1 CORINTHIANS 1:3

I am my
Beloved's
and my
Beloved
is mine.

Song of Songs 6:3

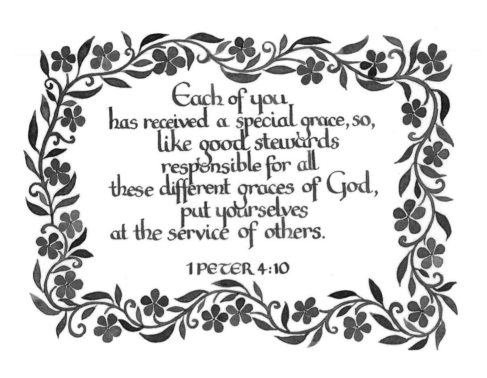

Each of you
has received a special grace, so,
like good stewards
responsible for all
these different graces of God,
put yourselves
at the service of others.

1 PETER 4:10

In
returning
and rest
you shall be
saved;
in quietness and
trust shall be
your strength.

ISAIAH 30:15

Have you seen him whom my soul loves?

song of songs 3:3

The Word
is very near
to you,
it is in
your mouth
and in
your heart
for your
observance.

DEUTERONOMY 30:14

YOU ARE MY
HIDING PLACE
O LORD

PSALM 31:7

I have told you
all this
so that you may
find peace
in ME.
In the world
you will have trouble,
but be brave:
I have
conquered
the world.

JOHN 16:33

I have said
these things to you
so that My joy
may be in you
and that your joy
may be complete.

John 15:11

ASK
AND IT WILL BE GIVEN
TO YOU;

SEARCH
AND YOU WILL FIND;

KNOCK
AND THE DOOR
WILL BE OPENED
TO YOU.

MATTHEW 7:7

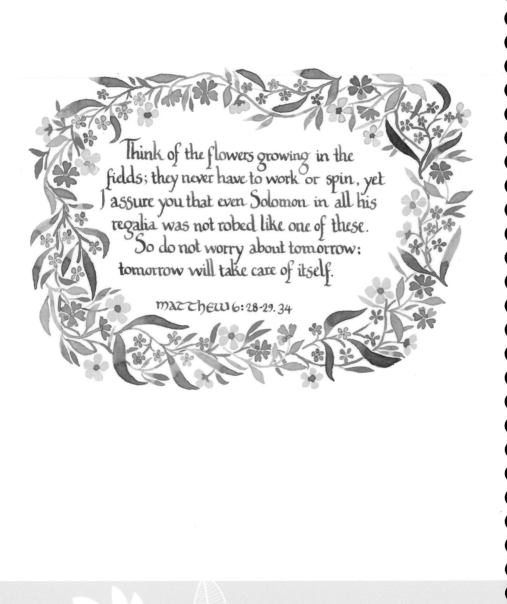

Think of the flowers growing in the fields; they never have to work or spin, yet I assure you that even Solomon in all his regalia was not robed like one of these. So do not worry about tomorrow: tomorrow will take care of itself.

MATTHEW 6: 28-29. 34

The SPIRIT helps us
in our weakness;
for we do not know how to pray
as we ought, but the Spirit
Himself intercedes for us
with sighs too deep for words.

Romans 8:26

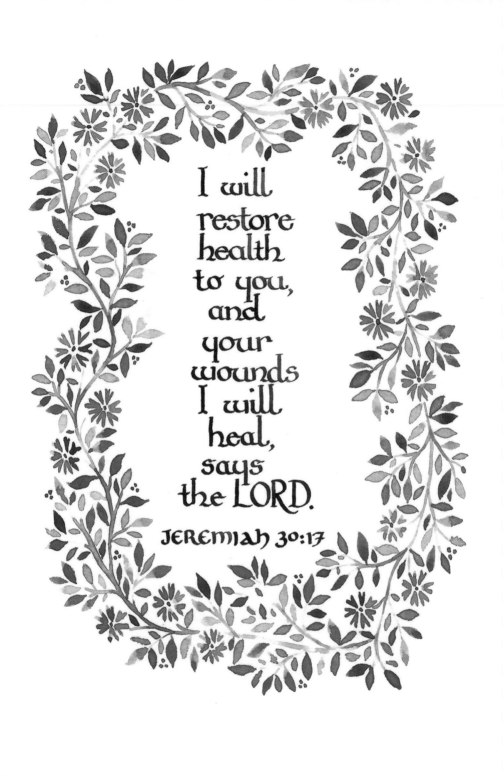

I will
restore
health
to you,
and
your
wounds
I will
heal,
says
the LORD.

JEREMIAH 30:17

THINK OF THE LOVE
THAT THE FATHER
HAS LAVISHED ON US
BY LETTING US
BE CALLED
GOD'S CHILDREN...

1 JOHN 3:1

Does a woman
forget her baby
at the breast,
or fail to cherish
the son of her womb?
Yet even if these forget,
I will never forget you...
for the mountains
may depart,
the hills be shaken,
but My love for you
will never leave you.

Isaiah 49:15;
54:10

As for Mary,
she TREASURED all these things
and PONDERED them
in her HEART.

LUKE 2:19

Make your home in Me
as I make Mine in you.
As a branch
cannot bear fruit
all by itself,
but must remain
part of the vine,
neither can you
unless you
remain in Me.
I am the vine,
you are the branches.

John 15:4-5

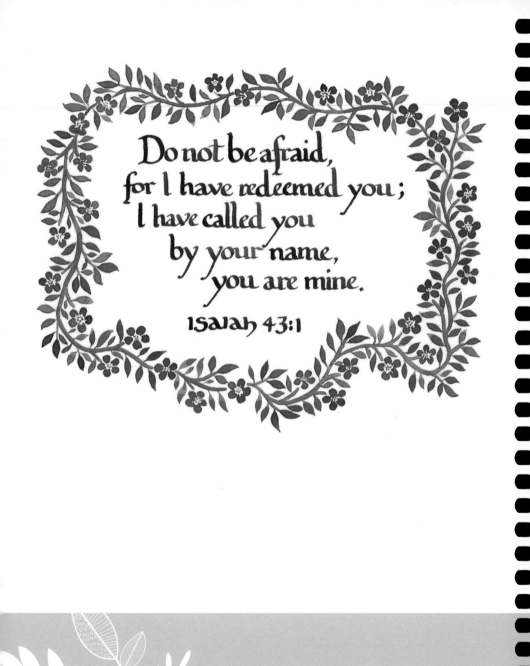

Do not be afraid,
for I have redeemed you;
I have called you
by your name,
you are mine.

Isaiah 43:1

The Lord is my shepherd;
there is nothing I shall want.
Fresh and green are the pastures
where He gives me repose.
Near restful waters He leads me,
to revive my drooping spirit.

He guides me along the right path;
He is true to His name.
If I should walk in the valley of darkness
no evil would I fear.
You are there with Your crook and Your staff;
With these You give me comfort.

You have prepared a banquet for me
In the sight of my foes.
My head You have anointed with oil
my cup is overflowing.

Surely goodness and kindness shall follow me
all the days of my life.
In the Lord's own house shall I dwell
for ever and ever.

PSALM 22 (23)

The LORD says this:
I have loved you with an
EVERLASTING LOVE,
so I am constant in my
affection for you.

JEREMIAH 31:3

my dove
hiding in
the clefts
of the rock
show me
your face
let me hear
your voice
for your
voice is sweet
and your face
is beautiful.

Song of Songs 2:14

Of You my heart has spoken:
"SEEK HIS FACE."
It is Your face, O Lord,
that I seek;
hide not Your face.

Psalm 26:8-9

Your WORD is a lamp for my steps and a light for my path.

PSALM 118:105

I have come
so that they may have
LIFE
and have it to the full.

John 10:10

I will sing a NEW SONG to my God.

Judith 16:13

The Lord is close
to the broken-hearted;
those whose spirit is crushed
he will save.

PSALM 33:18

The LORD came
to my help.
For me you have changed
my MOURNING
into DANCING...
So my soul
sings psalms to you
unceasingly,
O LORD my GOD,
I will THANK you
FOREVER.

PSALM 29:10-12

I can do
ALL THINGS
in Him
who strengthens me.

PHILIPPIANS 4:13

Love is always
patient & kind;
it is never jealous;
love is never
boastful or conceited;
it is never rude
or selfish;
it does not take offence,
and is not resentful.
Love takes no pleasure
in other people's sins
but delights in the truth;
it is always ready
to excuse,
to trust, to hope,
& to endure all things.
Love does not
come to an end.

1 CORINTHIANS 13:4-8

YOU WILL LEARN
THE TRUTH
AND THE TRUTH
WILL MAKE
YOU FREE.

John 8:32

Your body,
you know,
is a temple
of the

HOLY SPIRIT

1 Corinthians 6:19

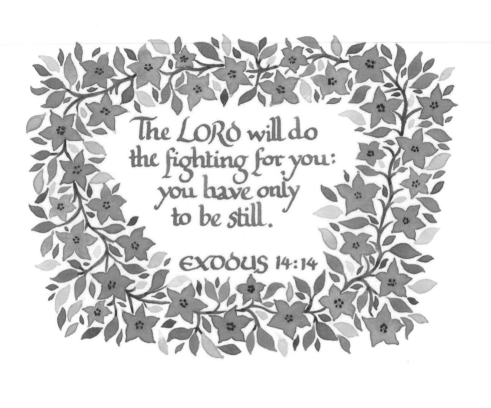

The LORD will do
the fighting for you:
you have only
to be still.

EXODUS 14:14

Seek the Lord
in simplicity
of heart;
he shows himself
to those
who do not
distrust
him.

WISDOM 1:1.2

THE joy OF THE LORD IS YOUR strength.

NEHEMIAH 8:10

You yourselves
have seen
how I carried you on
eagle's wings
and brought you
to MYSELF.

cf. Exodus 19:4

The LORD is very near.
There is no need to worry;
but if there is anything you need,
pray for it, asking GOD for it
with prayer and thanksgiving,
and the peace of GOD,
which is so much greater
than we can understand,
will guard your hearts and your
thoughts, in CHRIST JESUS.

Philippians 4:5-7

The LORD is KIND and full of compassion, slow to anger, abounding in LOVE.

psalm 144:8

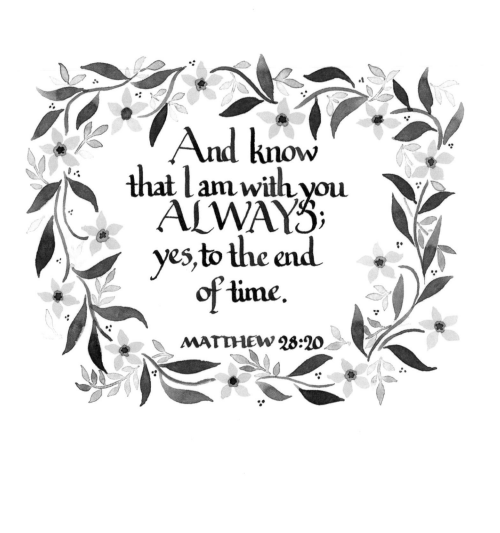

And know
that I am with you
ALWAYS;
yes, to the end
of time.

MATTHEW 28:20

The steadfast love of the LORD never ceases, His mercies never come to an end; they are new every morning; great is Thy faithfulness.

LAMENTATIONS 3:22-23

ALLELUIA!
O PRAISE THE LORD
ALL YOU NATIONS,
ACCLAIM HIM
ALL YOU PEOPLES.

PSALM 116:1

For I am CERTAIN
of this:
NEITHER death, nor life,
no angel, no prince,
NOTHING THAT EXISTS,
nothing still to come,
not ANY power,
or height or depth,
nor any created thing,
can EVER come
between us and
THE LOVE OF GOD
made visible in
JESUS CHRIST our Lord.

ROMANS 8:38-39

BEHOLD,
I MAKE
ALL THINGS
NEW.

REVELATION 21:5

The Word is a Light to my Path:
an illustrated prayer journal

Redemptorist Publications
Wolf's Lane, Chawton, Hampshire, GU34 3HQ, UK
Tel. +44 (0)1420 88222, Fax. +44 (0)1420 88805
Email rp@rpbooks.co.uk, www.rpbooks.co.uk

A registered charity limited by guarantee
Registered in England 03261721

Illustrations © Sr Lucy Cahill OP
Designed by Eliana Thompson

ISBN 978-0-85231-598-9

Printed by Lithgo Press Ltd., Leicester, LE8 6NU